THE NAILS WHO CRIED

Book I

of

The Creation Speaks Series

Shepherd House Books
1.877.745.3939
www.bookswithpurpose.com
Brenda Farthing © 2005
LCCN 2005906696
ISBN 0-9772033-0-1
USA

From the Author

When Jesus said, "Suffer little children, and forbid them not, to come unto me," I determined to do all that is within my gifting and ability to obey His desire.

I wanted to allow God's gift, through me, to draw the children to Jesus in a real and personal way.

If children are capable of responding to the call of Jesus, my desire is to clarify that call to them in ways they can understand.

I hope and pray that, in some small way, I can contribute to this most holy calling upon my life.

Brenda Farthing,
2005

Introduction

Shortly after writing this book, I heard an international televangelist/pastor say that he believed the gospel in America was diluted and void of the cross.

If this is the case, what an opportune time to instill in our children the foundational truth of the cross and the price that Jesus paid.

This book deals with the crucifixion. It doesn't go into any details, but only brings up the subject. After the story the parents can then discuss with their children the crucifixion and the resurrection as is appropriate for their child.

It is my hope that children will read or hear the Creation Speaks series and realize that even God's creation *may* have something to say. Creation Speaks is *their* testimony of what *they* saw and from *their* view. They not only share their story, but they do it through the style of rhyme. Rhyming will help the children memorize the story and thereby remember it!

Also, hidden in this book is a scripture reference to the crucifixion story. Help your children find the scripture and then read it to them from the Bible.

As with all the Creation Speaks series, the new characters from the next book will make an appearance on the last page. This, I hope, will arouse their curiosity as to what lies ahead in the next story.

Dedication

This series, Creation Speaks, is dedicated to my ten grandchildren: Brittany, Paige, Tiffany, Jesse, Courtney, Kelsey, Heather, Angel, Kalei, and Cheyenne.

These kids, because of their love of a story, have kept me on my toes to always deliver something fresh and new. I love them all very much. Also, to my husband Elmer, who always supports anything I endeavor to do.

And most of all, I thank the Lord Jesus for giving me any ability I may possess.

—Brenda Farthing, 2005

Thank you Ross, my drawing teacher, Erica, my good friend, and especially Brenda, who took the chance on me, for making this possible. Thank you Mom, for all your love, and thank you Dad for hanging in there with me through the good times and the bad.

—Nichole Edralin, 2005

The Nails Who Cried

Book I

of

The Creation Speaks Series

Written
by
Brenda Farthing

and

Illustrated
by
Nichole Edralin

WE NAILS WERE MADE

LIKE ALL THE REST...

HEATED AND

HAMMERED

TO STAND THE TEST.

WE WERE ALL
THROWN ASIDE...

UNTIL A NEW HOME
WE WOULD OCCUPY.

IT RAINED AND
SNOWED AND
COVERED US UP.

WE THOUGHT WE
WOULD RUST
AND BE WASHED UP.

WE WAITED AND
WONDERED FOR SUCH
A LONG TIME...

WOULD WE BE
CHOSEN...OR LEFT
BEHIND?

WE WONDERED IF WE
WOULD EVER BE FOUND,

AND GIVEN A JOB
THAT WE COULD BE
PROUD.

LITTLE DID WE KNOW
THAT OUR DAY WAS
SO NEAR,

WHEN WE WOULD BE
CHOSEN AND
TAKEN FROM HERE.

OUR DAY CAME
AND WE WERE BOUGHT
BY A SOLDIER.

THROWN IN A BAG,
WE TRAVELLED
A LITTLE FARTHER.

WHEN WE LEARNED
OF OUR FATE
WE STARTED TO CRY,

"WHY MUST WE BE THE
ONES
TO CRUCIFY?"

THEN WE HEARD A VOICE
THAT SEEMED TO SAY,

"DON'T FEEL SO SAD,
THINGS MIGHT LOOK BAD
TODAY."

"BUT KNOW FOR SURE
THAT OUR GOD HAS
A PLAN.

"BE HERE
IN THREE DAYS
TO SEE JESUS
RISE AGAIN!"

Look for these upcoming titles by the author
at
www.bookswithpurpose.com

Creation Speaks Series

The Nails Who Cried
The Rocks Had Praise
The Napkin
The Jordan River
The Ol'Ship

The Heavenlies Series